3 9100 00719 833 9

W9-BUJ-376

This book was lost and paid for at the library and then we also found it Again.

C.W
22/8/92

MOMMIES AT WORK

MOMMIES AT WORK

Written by
EVE MERRIAM

Illustrated by
BENI MONTRESOR

Alfred A. Knopf: New York

L.C. Catalog card number: 61-8126

THIS IS A BORZOI BOOK,
PUBLISHED BY ALFRED A. KNOPF, INC.

·····➤◆➤·····

Originally published in different form as "Mommies, Mommies" in *Charm.*

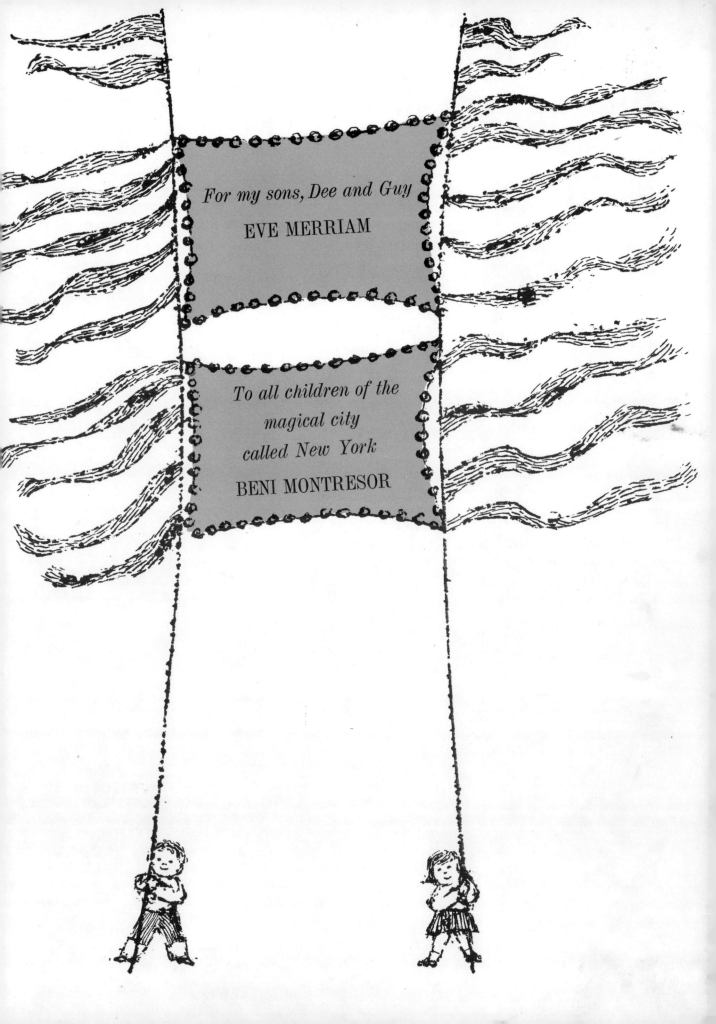

For my sons, Dee and Guy
EVE MERRIAM

To all children of the
magical city
called New York
BENI MONTRESOR

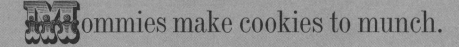ommies make cookies to munch.

Mommies have laps
to snuggle in.

Mommies wash dishes and necks and ears.

Tie shoelaces and hair ribbons.

Find mittens that are missing.

Kiss places that hurt and places that don't.

Zip you in and button you up and tuck in your favorite toys.

What other things
do mommies do?
All kinds of mommies do
all kinds of work.
In tall office buildings,

In spread-out ranches,

In radio repair shops,

Supermarkets,

All kinds of stores—

All kinds of mommies at all kinds of jobs.

There are dancer mommies.

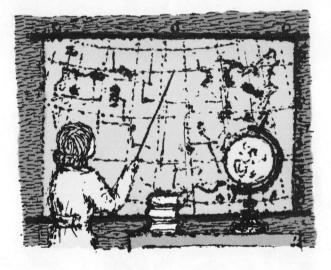

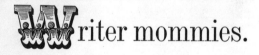 Writer mommies.

 eachers.

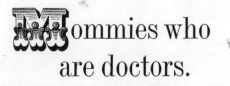 ommies who
are doctors.

Cashier mommies
counting up money
in banks.

Bridge-building mommies
with blueprints and T squares.

Television director mommies.

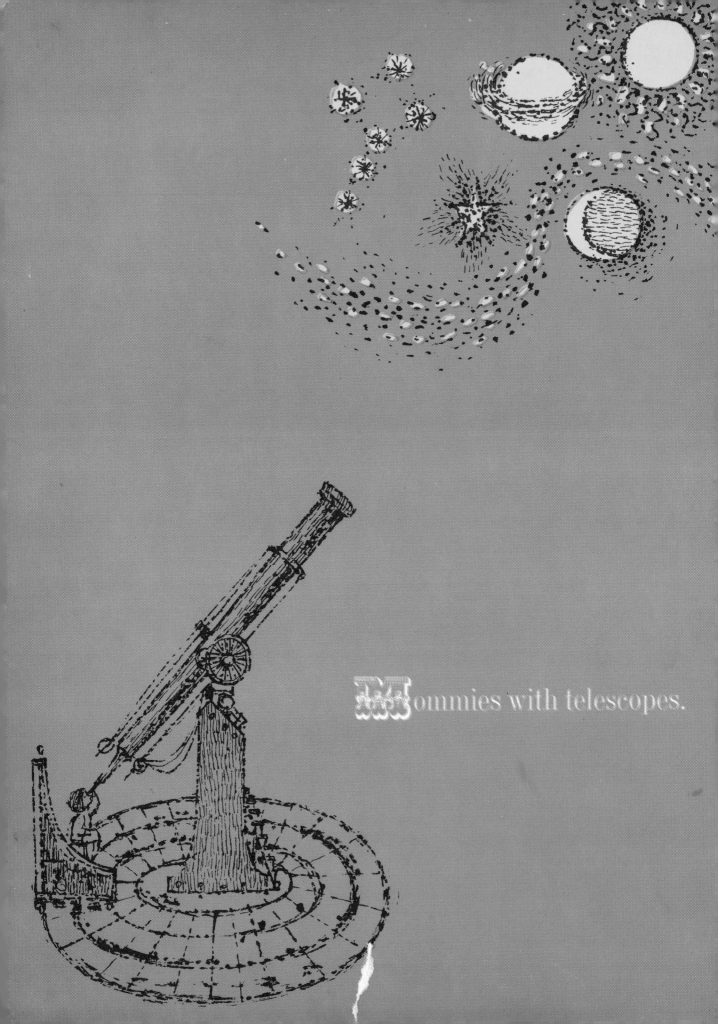

Mommies with telescopes.

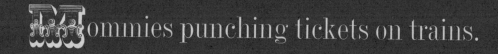
Mommies punching tickets on trains.

Mommies in pet shops.

Mommies selling hats at counters.

At soda fountains pouring out
chocolate ice-cream floats.

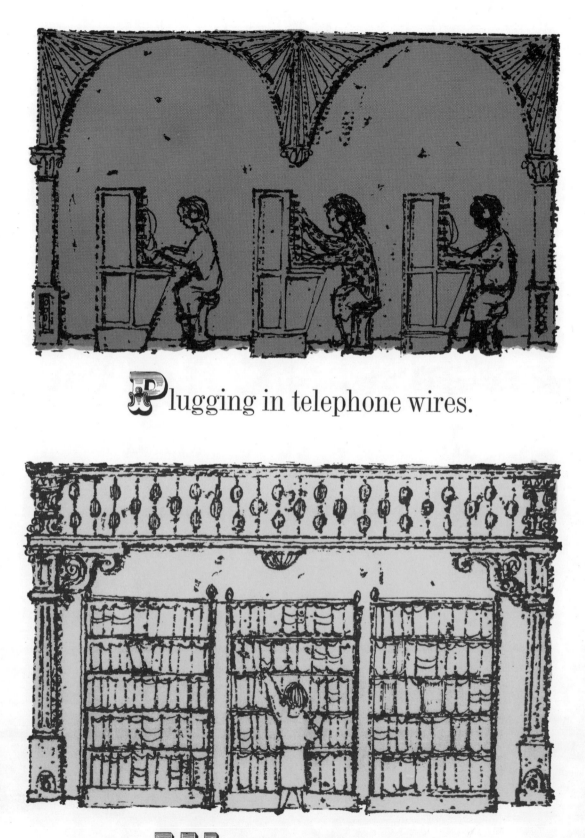

Plugging in telephone wires.

Working in libraries.

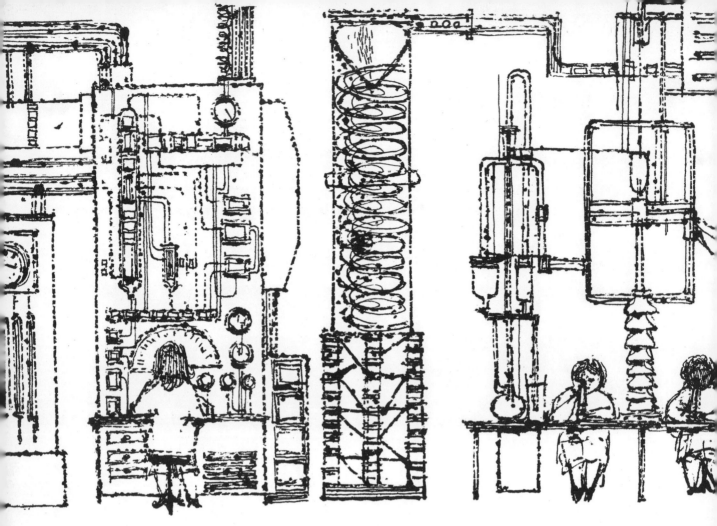

Atom-splitting mommies.

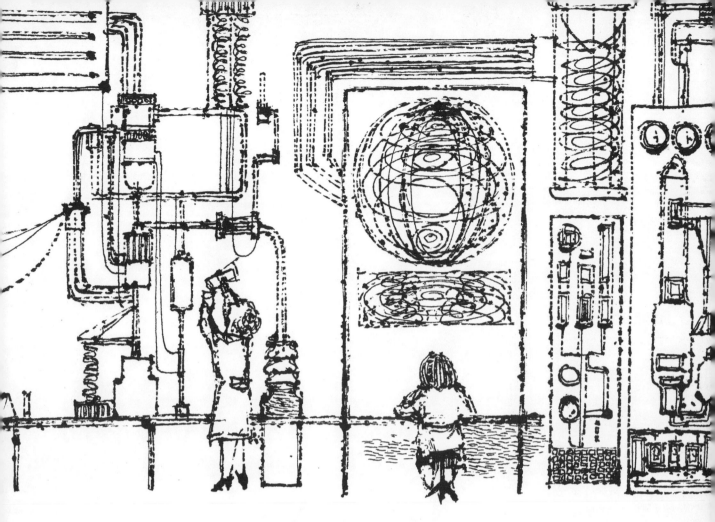

Assembly-line mommies building cars.

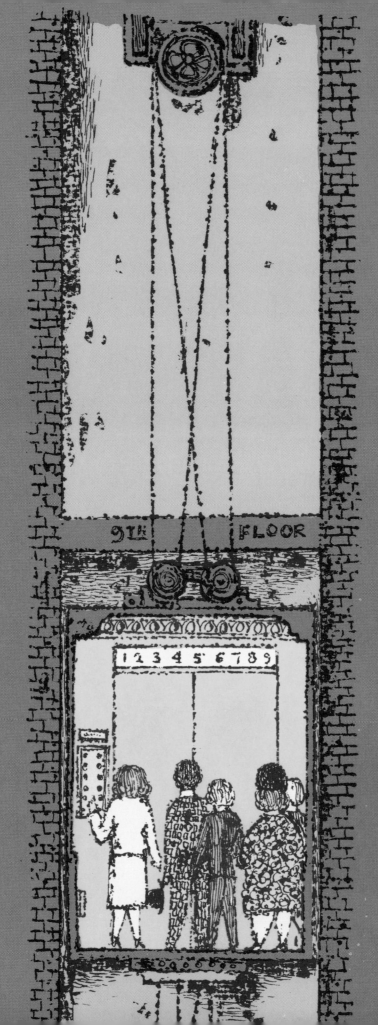

9TH FLOOR

1 2 3 4 5 6 7 8 9

Mommies
running
elevators.

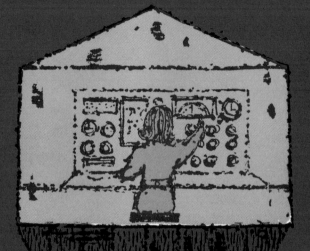

Sending signals
in airport towers.

Circus mommies walking tightropes.

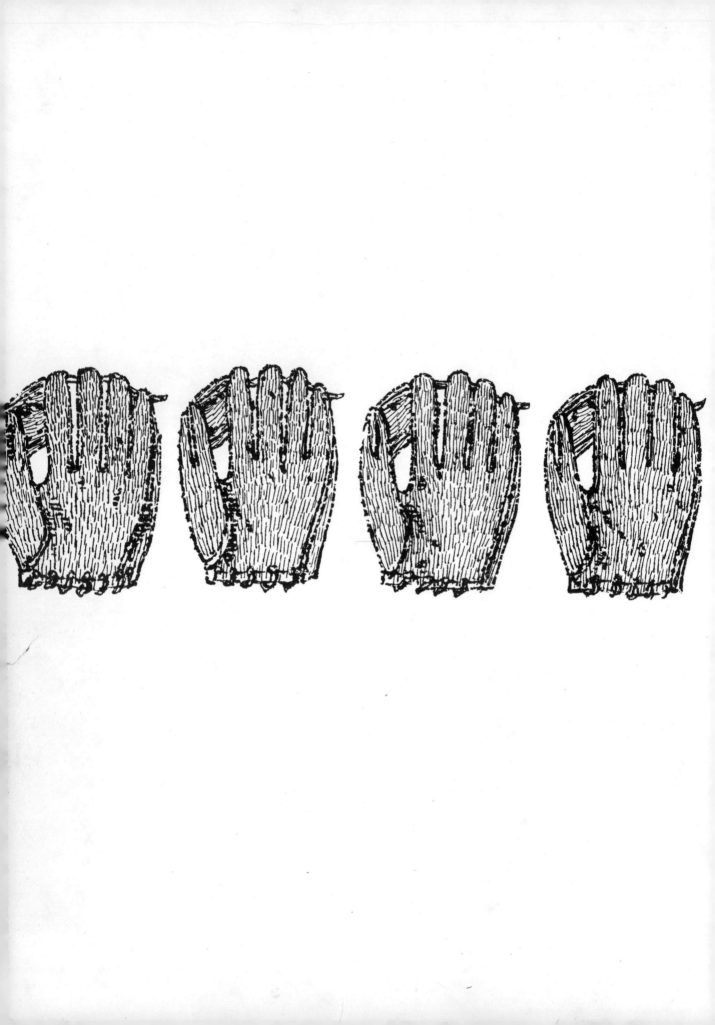

Factory mommies stitching baseball gloves—

and all mommies loving the best of all to be your very own mommy, and coming home to *you!*